This book belongs to:

......Heather......

......Bruns......

Bright Sparks books have been created
with the help of experts in early childhood education.
They are designed to help young children achieve
success in their early learning years.

Retold by Monica Hughes
Illustrated by Daniel Howarth

Reading consultants: Betty Root and Monica Hughes

First published by Parragon in 2007

Parragon
Queen Street House
4 Queen Street
Bath BA1 1HE, UK

ISBN 978-1-4054-9089-4

Printed in China

Rumpelstiltskin

Bath New York Singapore Hong Kong Cologne Delhi Melbourne

Helping your child read

Bright Sparks readers are closely linked to recognized learning strategies. Their vocabulary has been carefully selected from word lists recommended by educational experts.

Read the story

Read the story to your child a few times.

> The miller's daughter began to cry.
> Then she saw the little man.
> "What will you give me if I help you?" he said.
> "I will give you my ring," she said.

Follow your finger

Run your finger under the text as you read. Soon your child will begin to follow the words with you.

Look at the pictures

Talk about the pictures. They will help your child understand the story.

"What will you give me?" 17

Give it a try

Let your child try reading the large type on each right-hand page. It repeats a line from the story.

Join in

When your child is ready, encourage him or her to join in with the main story text. Shared reading is the first step to reading alone.

Once upon a time there was a miller.
The miller had a daughter.
One day the king rode by.
"My daughter can spin straw into
gold," the miller told the king.

The miller had a daughter.

So the king took the miller's daughter to his castle.
He took her to a room full of straw.
"Spin this straw into gold," said the king.
Then he left her alone all night.

"Spin this straw into gold."

The miller's daughter could not spin
straw into gold.

She began to cry.

But then she saw a little man.

"I can spin straw into gold," he said.

"What will you give me if I help you?"

"I will give you my necklace," said the
miller's daughter.

She saw a little man.

In the morning the little man was gone, and the room was full of gold.

The king came to see the miller's daughter.
He was very pleased.
The king took her to a big room.
The room was full of straw.
"Spin this straw into gold," said the king.
Then he left her alone all night.

The room was full of straw.

The miller's daughter began to cry.
Then she saw the little man.
"What will you give me if I help you?"
he said.
"I will give you my ring," she said.

"What will you give me?"

In the morning the little man was gone, and the room was full of gold.

The king came to see the miller's daughter.
He was very pleased.
The king took the miller's daughter to a bigger room full of straw.
"Spin this straw into gold, and I will marry you," said the king.
Then he left her alone all night.

"Spin this straw into gold."

19

The miller's daughter began to cry.
Then she saw the little man.
"What will you give me if I help you?"
he said.
"I have nothing to give you," she said.
"I will help you again," said the little
man, "but you must give me your first
baby."

"I have nothing to give you."

In the morning the little man was gone,
and the room was full of gold.
The king married the miller's daughter.

Soon the queen had a baby.
She forgot all about the little man.
One day the little man came to take
the baby.
The queen began to cry.
"I will not take your baby if you can
guess my name," he said. "I will come
back in the morning."

The queen had a baby.

That night the queen went for a walk
in the woods.
She tried to guess the little man's name.
"Is it Don or Ron?" she said to herself.
"Is it Bill or Will?"
Then she saw the little man.
He was dancing around a fire, singing:

"My name is Rumpelstiltskin.
Rumpelstiltskin is my name."

She saw the little man.

In the morning the little man came to see the queen.

"Is your name Don or Ron?" said the queen.

"No! No! No!" said the little man.

"Is your name Bill or Will?" said the queen.

"No! No! No!" said the little man.

Then the queen said, "Is your name Rumpelstiltskin?"

"Yes! Yes! Yes!" said the little man, and off he ran.

And they never saw Rumpelstiltskin again.

They never saw
Rumpelstiltskin again.

Look back in your book.
Can you read these words?

daughter

king

little man

straw

gold

Can you answer these questions?

Who asked the
miller's daughter to
spin straw into gold?

What did the miller's
daughter give to the
little man?

What was the little
man's name?

The End